THE HOUSE THAT JACK BUILT

ILLUSTRATED BY
RANDOLPH CALDECOTT

SBN 0-88302-315-6

THE MULBERRY PRESS, INC. • NEW YORK

THE HOUSE
THAT JACK BUILT

THIS is the House that Jack built.

This is the Malt,
That lay in the House that Jack built.

This is the Rat,
That ate the Malt,
That lay in the House that Jack built.

This is the Cat,
That killed the Rat,
That ate the Malt,
That lay in the House that Jack built.

This is the Dog,
That worried the Cat,
That killed the Rat,
That ate the Malt,
That lay in the House that Jack built.

This is the Cow with the crumpled horn,
That tossed the Dog,
That worried the Cat,
That killed the Rat,
That ate the Malt,
That lay in the House that Jack built.

This is the Maiden all forlorn,
That milked the Cow with the crumpled horn,
That tossed the Dog,
That worried the Cat,
That killed the Rat,
That ate the Malt,
That lay in the House that Jack built.

This is the Man all tattered and torn,
That kissed the Maiden all forlorn,
That milked the Cow with the crumpled horn,
That tossed the Dog,
That worried the Cat,
That killed the Rat,
That ate the Malt,
That lay in the House that Jack built.

This is the Priest, all shaven and shorn,
That married the Man all tattered and torn,
That kissed the Maiden all forlorn,
That milked the Cow with the crumpled horn,
That tossed the Dog,
That worried the Cat,
That killed the Rat,
That ate the Malt,
That lay in the House that Jack built.

This is the Cock that crowed in the morn,
That waked the Priest all shaven and shorn,
That married the Man all tattered and torn,
That kissed the Maiden all forlorn,
That milked the Cow with the crumpled horn,
That tossed the Dog,
That worried the Cat,
That killed the Rat,
That ate the Malt,
That lay in the House that Jack built.

This is the Farmer who sowed the corn,
That fed the Cock that crowed in the morn,
That waked the Priest all shaven and shorn,
That married the Man all tattered and torn,
That kissed the Maiden all forlorn,
That milked the Cow with the crumpled horn,
That tossed the Dog,
That worried the Cat,
That killed the Rat,
That ate the Malt,
That lay in the House that Jack built.

THE FARMER'S BOY

WHEN I was a farmer, a Farmer's Boy,
    I used to keep my master's HORSES,
With a GEE-wo here, and a GEE-wo there,
    And here a GEE, and there a GEE,
        And everywhere a GEE;
Says I, My pretty lass, will you come to the banks
    of the Aire oh?

When I was a farmer, a Farmer's Boy,
   I used to keep my master's LAMBS,
With a Baa-baa here, and a Baa-baa there,
   And here a Baa, and there a Baa,
   And everywhere a Baa;
With a Gee-wo here, and a Gee-wo there,
   And here a Gee, and there a Gee,
   And everywhere a Gee;
Says I, My pretty lass, will you come to the banks
   of the Aire oh?

When I was a farmer, a Farmer's Boy,
    I used to keep my master's HENS,
With a CHUCK-CHUCK here, and a CHUCK-CHUCK there,
    And here a CHUCK, and there a CHUCK,
    And everywhere a CHUCK;
With a BAA-BAA here, and a BAA-BAA there,
    And here a BAA, and there a BAA,
    And everywhere a BAA;
With a GEE-WO here, and a GEE-WO there,
      &c., &c., &c.
Says I, My pretty lass, will you come to the banks
    of the Aire oh?

When I was a farmer, a Farmer's Boy,
    I used to keep my master's PIGS,
With a GRUNT-GRUNT here, and a GRUNT-GRUNT there,
        And here a GRUNT, and there a GRUNT,
        And everywhere a GRUNT;
With a CHUCK-CHUCK here, and a CHUCK-CHUCK there,
        And here a CHUCK, and there a CHUCK,
        And everywhere a CHUCK;
With a BAA-BAA here, and a BAA-BAA there,
            &c.,   &c.,   &c.
With a GEE-wo here, and a GEE-wo there.
            &c.,   &c.,   &c.
Says I, My pretty lass, will you come to the banks
        of the Aire oh?

When I was a farmer, a Farmer's Boy,
    I used to keep my master's DUCKS,
With a QUACK-QUACK here, and a QUACK-QUACK there,
    And here a QUACK, and there a QUACK,
    And everywhere a QUACK;
With a GRUNT-GRUNT here, and a GRUNT-GRUNT there,
    &c., &c., &c.
With a CHUCK-CHUCK here, &c.
    With a BAA-BAA here, &c.
With a GEE-wo here, &c.
Says I, My pretty lass, will you come to the banks
    of the Aire oh?

When I was a farmer, a Farmer's Boy,
    I used to keep my master's DOGS,
With a Bow-bow here, and a Bow-wow there,
    And here a Bow, and there a Wow,
    And everywhere a Wow;
With a Quack-quack here, and a Quack-quack there,
    &c., &c., &c.
With a Grunt-grunt here, &c.
With a Chuck-chuck here, &c.
With a Baa-baa here, &c.
With a Gee-wo here, &c.
Says I, My pretty lass, will you come to the banks
    of the Aire oh?

When I was a farmer, a Farmer's Boy,
    I used to keep my master's CHILDREN,
With a Shouting here, and a Pouting there,
    And here a Shout, and there a Pout,
    And everywhere a Shout;
With a Bow-bow here, and a Bow-wow there,
        &c., &c., &c.
With a Quack-quack here, &c.
With a Grunt-grunt here, &c.
With a Chuck-chuck here, &c.
With a Baa-baa here, &c.
With a Gee-wo here, &c.
Says I, My pretty lass, will you come to the banks
        of the Aire oh?

When I was a farmer, a Farmer's Boy,
　　I used to keep my master's TURKEYS,
With a GOBBLE-GOBBLE here, and a GOBBLE-GOBBLE there,
　　And here a GOBBLE, and there a GOBBLE;
　　And everywhere a GOBBLE;
With a SHOUTING here, and a POUTING there,
　　　&c., 　　&c., 　　&c.
With a Bow-wow here, &c.
With a QUACK-QUACK here, &c.
With a GRUNT-GRUNT here, &c.
With a CHUCK-CHUCK here, &c.
With a BAA-BAA here, &c.
With a GEE-wo here, &c.
Says I, My pretty lass, will you come to the banks
　　of the Aire oh?